MW00789000

ISBN 979-8-9876344-3-1

info@captaintimpublishing.com
www.captaintimpublishing.com

EATING HEALTHY
WITH **DR. FRANCIS**

SUPERFOOD SOUPS

Dr. A. Francis

February | 2023

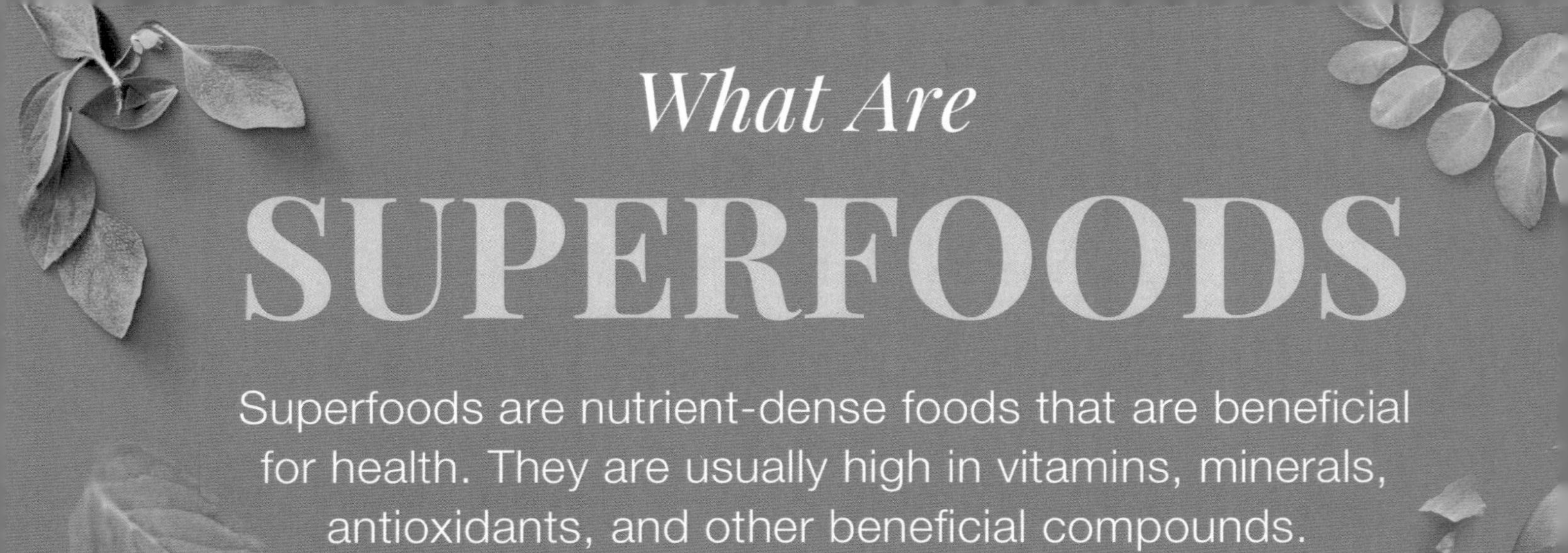

What Are

SUPERFOODS

Superfoods are nutrient-dense foods that are beneficial for health. They are usually high in vitamins, minerals, antioxidants, and other beneficial compounds.

Benefits of Superfood Soups

- Power packed with nutrients
- Quick & easy to cook
- Good for your digestion
- Improved diet quality
- Natural healing power

CONTENTS

Superfoods

Soup Recipes

Health Benefits of

WHEATGRASS

May support immune system

May reduce inflammation

Helps reduce food cravings

High in nutrients and antioxidants

Helps to detoxify your system

May reduce cholesterol

May aid in weight loss

May aid in blood sugar regulation

HOW TO EAT & DRINK

Blend
into a smoothie

Juice
wheatgrass

Bake
with wheatgrass

Cook
soups & sauces

Antioxidant-Rich Wheatgrass

AVOCADO SOUP

- 2 cups spinach
- Water, as needed
- 2 sprigs fresh mint
- 2 avocado
- 2 cups almond milk
- 4 tsp chia seeds
- 2-3 handfuls arugula
- 4 tsp wheatgrass powder

Blend all ingredients together in a blender, except chia. Add water if your soup seems too thick. Add the chia and mix it in again. Serve cold.

4
Servings

8
ingredients

2 min
to cook

Health Benefits of

SEA MOSS

May support thyroid function

May support heart health

May reduce inflammation

Supports muscle recovery

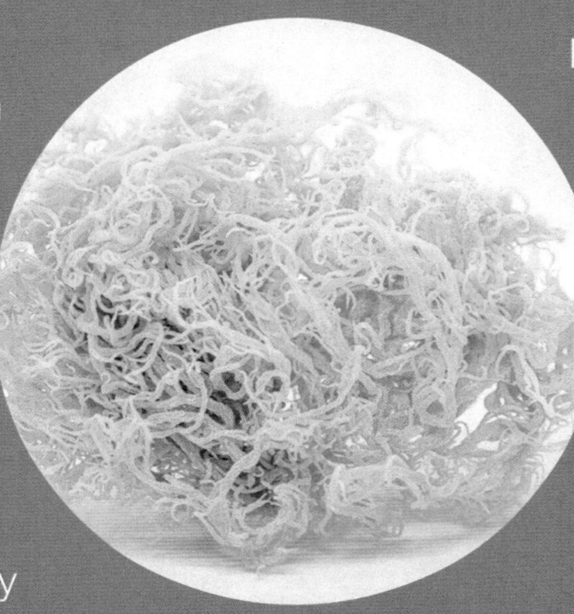

Helps maintain a healthy weight

May support gut health

May improve skin health

May support immune system

HOW TO EAT & DRINK

Blend
into a smoothie

Brew
sea moss tea

Make
seamoss jam

Cook
soups & sauces

Nutrient-Rich Sea Moss

CARIBBEAN SOUP

- 3 carrots
- 1 tsp turmeric
- 3 cloves garlic
- 1 cup broccoli
- ¼ cabbage head
- 3 tbsp sea moss gel
- ¼ cup black eye peas
- 4 cups vegetable broth
- 1 cup sweet potatoes
- 2 tsp ginger powder
- ½ tsp ground allspice
- 1 cup sliced potatoes

Chop the vegetables. Add broth, potatoes, peas in a pot. Cook 10 min. Add cabbage, carrots, broccoli, garlic, ginger, turmeric, all spices, salt to taste. Cook 15 min. Add sea moss gel, stir well.

4
Servings

12
ingredients

25 min
to cook

Health Benefits of TURMERIC

May reduce inflammation

May improve memory

May help delay aging

May support immune system

Can potentially reduce pain

Fights free radicals

May support heart health

May help with depression

HOW TO EAT & DRINK

Blend
into a smoothie

Add
to rice

Make
golden milk tea

Cook
soups & sauces

Immunity-Boosting Turmeric
CARROT SOUP

- 1 tbsp olive oil
- 1 onion, diced
- 3 carrots, diced
- ¾ cup plain yogurt
- 4 cups chicken broth
- 1 clove garlic, minced
- 1 ½ tbsp minced ginger
- 1 cup broccoli florets
- ½ cup red bell pepper, diced
- 1 tsp turmeric powder

Saute onion, garlic, bell pepper with oil until tender. Add remaining ingredients (except yogurt), simmer for 15 minutes. Puree soup with an immersion blender until creamy. Stir in yogurt.

4
Servings

10
ingredients

20 min
to cook

Health Benefits of

MORINGA

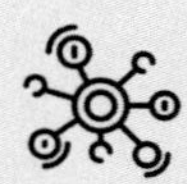
Rich in vitamins and minerals

May reduce inflammation

Rich in antioxidants

May aid in blood sugar regulation

Helps to detoxify your system

May support liver health

May support bone health

Good for nervous system

HOW TO EAT & DRINK

Blend
into a smoothie

Sprinkle
on salads

Bake
with moringa

Cook
soups & sauces

Gut Healthy Moringa
MISO SOUP

- 6 oz tofu
- 1 onion, sliced
- 1 zucchini, diced
- 2 tbsp green onion
- 2 cups kale shredded
- 4 cups vegetable broth
- 3 tbsp miso paste
- 1 tbsp moringa powder

Add zucchini and onion to a pot. Saute with 2 tbsp of water until softened. Add broth, tofu, miso paste. Cook 2 min. Remove from heat, add moringa powder, kale and stir. Serve with green onions.

4
Servings

8
ingredients

5 min
to cook

Health Benefits of
SPIRULINA

May improve digestive health

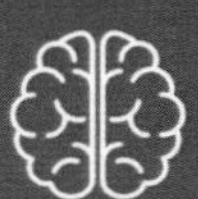
May support brain health

May support heart health

May support immune system

May help manage blood pressure

May improve anemia

Aids acne treatment

Rich in many nutrients

HOW TO EAT & DRINK

Blend
into a smoothie

Make
hummus

Add
in energy balls

Cook
soups & sauces

Super Healthy and Nutritious

SPIRULINA SOUP

- 2 tsp spirulina
- 1 tbsp lime juice
- 1 tsp fennel seeds
- 1 head of broccoli
- 1 zucchini, chopped
- 3 cups vegetable broth
- ¼ tsp ginger powder
- 2 cups spinach
- 2 sticks celery, diced
- 1 cup coconut milk
- 3 cloves garlic
- 1 medium onion

Add fennel seeds, onion, garlic, celery, broccoli to a pot, cook 4 min, add salt to taste, broth, zucchini, ginger. Simmer 10 min. Add milk, spinach, cook 1 min. Add lime juice, spirulina. Puree with immersion blender.

4
Servings

12
ingredients

15 min
to cook

Health Benefits of GINGER

May improve digestion

May support heart health

Relieves nausea

May support immune system

May support brain health
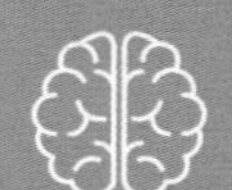

Fights fungal infections

Can heal irritated skin

May aid in blood sugar regulation

HOW TO EAT & DRINK

Blend
into a smoothie

Brew
ginger tea

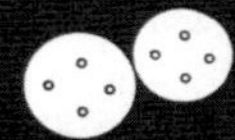
Bake
ginger cookies

Cook
soups & sauces

Anti-Inflammatory

GINGER SOUP

- 1 tbsp olive oil
- 1 onion, diced
- 3 cloves garlic
- 1 tbsp ginger
- 4 cups vegetable broth
- 1 large carrot, diced
- ¼ tsp turmeric
- ¼ tsp cumin

- ¼ tsp coriander
- ½ cup coconut milk
- 1 cup pumpkin, cubes

Add olive oil, onion, garlic, ginger, cook 5 min. Add broth, and spices, carrot, pumpkin, salt to taste. Bring to a boil, simmer for 20 min. Blend until smooth. Stir in coconut milk.

4
Servings

11
ingredients

25 min
to cook

Health Benefits of

CHIA SEEDS

May support heart health

May support bone health

May support digestive health

Help keep you full and satisfied

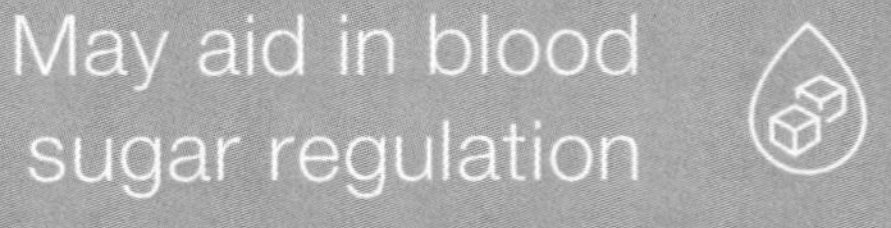
May aid in blood sugar regulation

May improve skin health

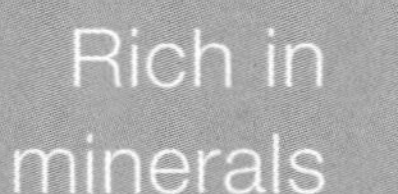
Rich in minerals

Great source of omega fatty acids

HOW TO EAT & DRINK

Blend
into smoothie

Make
chia pudding

Sprinkle
over foods

Cook
soups & sauces

Gut-Friendly Chia Seed

MUSHROOM SOUP

- ½ tbsp olive oil
- 1 onion, chopped
- ½ tsp dried thyme
- 2 tbsp chia seeds
- 2 cloves garlic, minced
- ¼ cup nutritional yeast
- 2 cups mushrooms, sliced
- 4 cups vegetable broth
- 1 cup spinach, chopped

Add the onion, oil, garlic to a pot sauté 3 min. Add mushrooms, cook 3 min. Add thyme, salt to taste, spinach, chia seeds, broth. Simmer 15 min. Add nutritional yeast (powder or flakes), stir.

4
Servings

9
ingredients

20 min
to cook

Health Benefits of

FLAX SEEDS

Great source of omega fatty acids

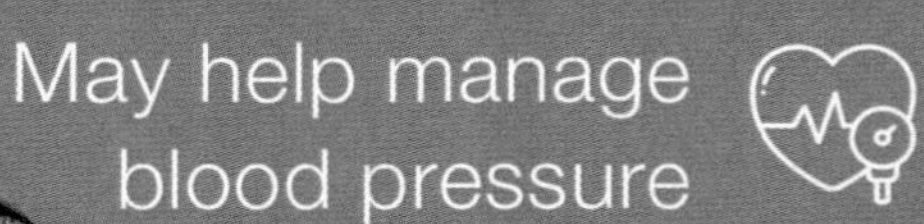

May help manage blood pressure

May support heart health

Loaded with nutrients

Help maintain a healthy weight

May relieve constipation

May aid in blood sugar regulation

Help reduce skin inflammation

HOW TO EAT & DRINK

Blend
into smoothie

Mix
with oatmeal

Add
over foods

Cook
soups

Heart-Healthy Flax seed

CELERY SOUP

- 1 tbsp olive oil
- 1 onion, diced
- 1 carrot, diced
- 2 potatoes, diced
- 3 cloves garlic, minced
- 2 celery stalks, diced
- 2 tbsp ground flax seeds
- 2 tbsp tomato paste
- 2 tbsp fresh parsley, chopped
- 4 cups vegetable broth

Add oil, onion, garlic, carrot, and celery to a pot, cook 5 minutes. Add potatoes, salt to taste, flax seeds, cook 5 min. Add tomato paste, vegetable broth, simmer 15 min. Serve with parsley.

4
Servings

10
ingredients

25 min
to cook

Health Benefits of

REISHI MUSHROOMS

May support immune system

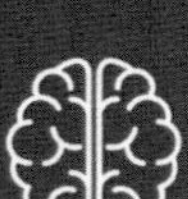
May support brain health

May lower blood pressure

Have allergy-fighting potential

May alleviate stress and fatigue

May support liver health

May improve sleep

May lower cholesterol levels

HOW TO USE REISHI POWDER

Blend
into a smoothie

Brew
Reishi tea

Add
to coffee

Cook
soups & sauces

Immunity-Boosting Reishi

REISHI SOUP

- 1 tbsp olive oil
- 1 leek, sliced
- 1 tbsp rice wine
- 2 tbsp tamari sauce
- 2 tbsp miso paste
- 4 cups vegetable broth
- 2 tbsp grated ginger
- 2 cloves garlic, minced
- 2 tbsp fresh parsley, chopped
- ¼ cup dried reishi mushrooms

Add the leek, oil, garlic to a pot, sauté 5 min. Add broth, reishi mushrooms, tamari sauce, miso paste, rice wine, ginger, simmer 15 min. Remove from heat and stir in parsley.

4
Servings

10
ingredients

20 min
to cook

Health Benefits of

BROCCOLI SPROUTS

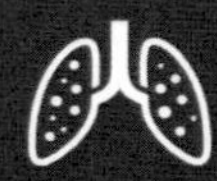
May help protect lungs

May support immune system

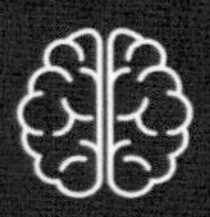
May support mental health

May reduce inflammation

May support gut health

May support heart health

Protect your skin from sun damage

May help prevent premature aging

HOW TO EAT & DRINK

Blend
into smoothie

Top
salads

Add
to wraps, toast

Cook
soups & sauces

HEALING SOUP

with Broccoli Sprouts

- 1 tbsp olive oil
- 1 tsp grated ginger
- 1 red onion, diced
- ¼ cup coconut milk
- 2 cloves garlic, minced
- 4 cups vegetable broth
- 2 cups broccoli sprouts
- 1 cup bell pepper, chopped

Add onion, garlic, oil to a pot, cook 5 min. Add ginger, broth, broccoli sprouts, bell pepper, salt to taste. Simmer for 10 min. Stir in coconut milk.

4
Servings

8
ingredients

15 min
to cook

Health Benefits of

HEMP SEEDS

May support immune system

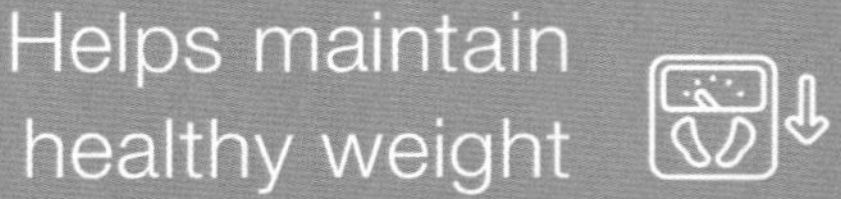

Helps maintain healthy weight

May support heart health

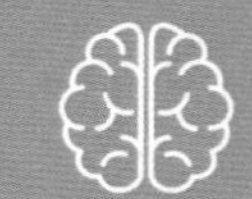

May support brain health

May improve skin health

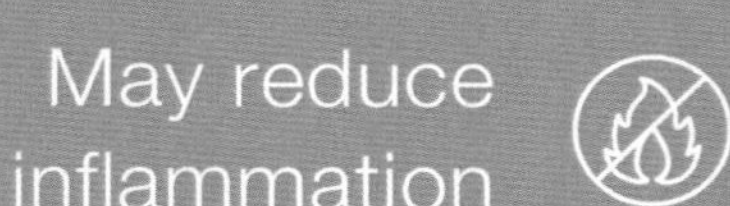

May reduce inflammation

May support digestive health

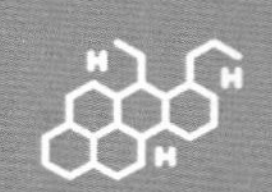

May regulate the hormone imbalances

HOW TO EAT & DRINK

Blend into smoothie

Sprinkle on salads

Make hemp milk

Cook soups & sauces

Nourishing Hemp Seed LENTIL SOUP

- 1 tbsp olive oil
- 1 small onion, diced
- 1 tsp dried oregano
- 2 carrots, diced
- 2 stalks celery, diced
- 1 tsp ground cumin
- 2 cloves garlic, minced
- 2 tbsp hemp seeds
- 1 tsp smoked paprika
- 1 cup red lentils
- 4 cups vegetable broth

Add onion, garlic, carrots, oil, celery to a pot, cook 8 min. Add cumin, oregano, smoked paprika, salt to taste, cook 1 min. Add lentils, broth. Simmer 30 min. Stir in hemp seeds.

4
Servings

11
ingredients

40 min
to cook

Health Benefits of
BUCKWHEAT

May support immune system

May improve digestion

Provides energy

May support heart health

May aid in blood sugar regulation

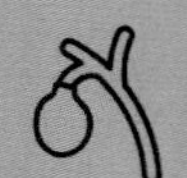
May help avoid gallstones

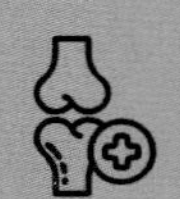
May support bone health

May help prevent premature aging

HOW TO EAT & DRINK

Make a 'porridge'

Top salads

Bake bread

Cook soups

Gut-Friendly Buckwheat COCONUT SOUP

- 1 tbsp olive oil
- 2 carrots, diced
- 2 onions, chopped
- 1 tsp ground ginger
- 2 cloves garlic, minced
- 2 celery stalks, diced
- 2 cups vegetable broth
- 1 cup buckwheat
- 1 tsp ground turmeric
- 1½ cups light coconut milk

Add onions, oil, garlic to a pot, cook 2 min. Add carrots, celery, broth, buckwheat, turmeric, ginger. Simmer 18 min. Stir in coconut milk, season with salt and pepper to taste.

4
Servings

10
ingredients

20 min
to cook

Health Benefits of

AMLA

May help manage blood pressure

May support eye health

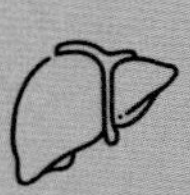
May support liver health

May support heart health

May improve digestion

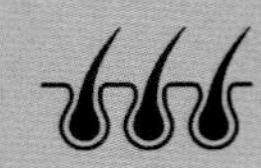
May increase hair growth

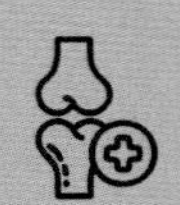
May support bone health

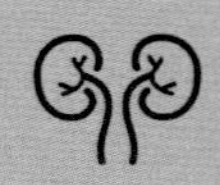
Helps improve kidney health

HOW TO EAT & DRINK

Pickle amla

Add to salads

Mix amla juice with water

Cook soups

Ayurvedic Healing Amla

CHICKPEA SOUP

- 1 tbsp olive oil
- 1 tsp ground cumin
- 1 tsp ground ginger
- ½ cup plain yogurt
- 1 large onion, chopped
- 1 tsp fresh coriander
- 2 carrots, chopped
- 1 cup fresh amla, diced
- 2 cups canned chickpeas
- 4 cups vegetable broth

Add the onion, oil to a pot, cook 2 min. Add coriander, cumin, ginger, carrots, salt to taste. Add chickpeas, amla, cook 3 min. Add broth, simmer 15 min. Serve with yogurt.

4
Servings

10
ingredients

20 min
to cook

Health Benefits of
QUINOA

May help prevent osteoporosis

May support heart health

May reduce inflammation

May improve skin health

May aid in blood sugar regulation

May improve anemia

May improve digestion

Helps maintain a healthy weight

HOW TO EAT & DRINK

Make
a 'porridge'

Top
salads

Bake
with quinoa

Cook
soups

Rich in Nutrients

QUINOA SOUP

- 1 tbsp olive oil
- 1 onion, diced
- ½ cup frozen corn
- 1 tsp ground cumin
- 2 red bell peppers, diced
- 1 tsp smoked paprika
- 4 cups vegetable broth
- 1 cup quinoa
- 1 can (15 oz) tomatoes
- 1 can (15 oz) black beans

Add onion, oil to a pot, cook 5 min. Add cumin, smoked paprika, and cook for 1 min. Add broth, tomatoes, quinoa, bell peppers. Simmer 15 min. Add corn, beans, cook 5 min.

4
Servings

10
ingredients

26 min
to cook

Health Benefits of

AMARANTH

May lower cholesterol levels

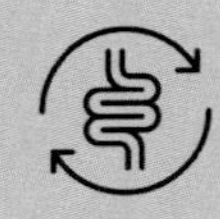
May improve digestion

May reduce inflammation

May support eye health

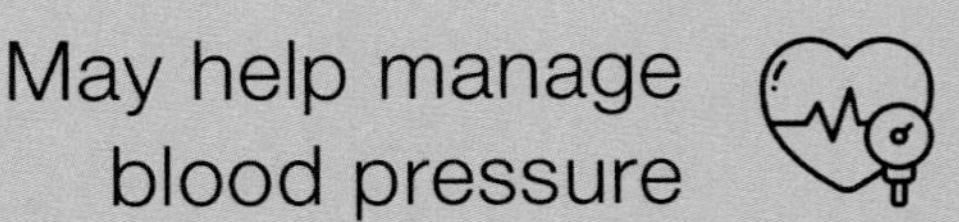
May help manage blood pressure

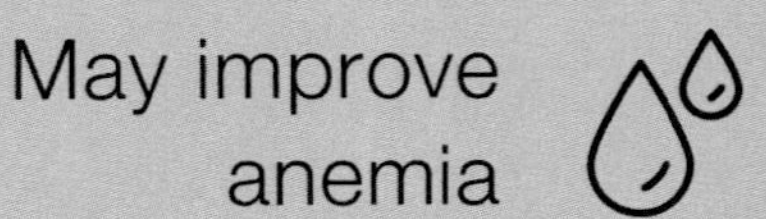
May improve anemia

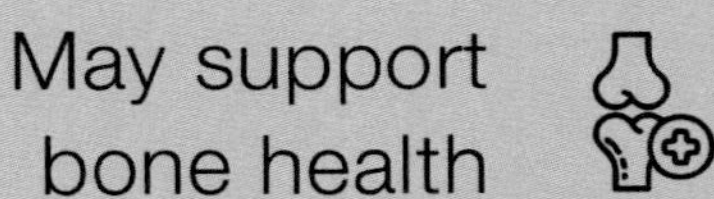
May support bone health

Helps maintain a healthy weight

HOW TO EAT & DRINK

Make
a 'porridge'

Top
salads

Bake
bread

Cook
soups

Nutritious AMARANTH SOUP

- 2 tbsp olive oil
- 1 small onion, diced
- 1 tsp turmeric powder
- 1 cup amaranth
- 4 cups vegetable broth
- 2 large carrots, diced
- 1 bell pepper, chopped
- 1 can diced tomatoes
- 2 tbsp tomato paste
- ¼ tsp red pepper flakes

Add the onion, oil to a pot, cook 5 min. Add turmeric, amaranth, pour in broth, simmer for 10 min. Add carrots, bell pepper, tomatoes, tomato paste, pepper flakes, salt to taste. Simmer 15 min.

4
Servings

10
ingredients

25 min
to cook

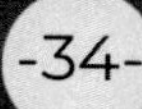

Health Benefits of

CAMU-CAMU

May support immune system

May improve oral health

May support heart health

May help with iron absorption

May help manage blood pressure
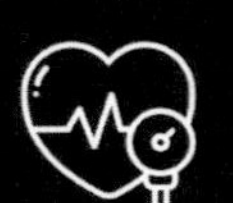

May help delay aging

Support healthy mood

May support eye health

HOW TO USE CAMU-CAMU POWDER

Blend
into smoothie

Bake
with powder

Make
energy balls

Cook
soups & sauces

Rich in Vitamin C

CAMU BEET SOUP

- 1 tbsp coconut oil
- 1 tsp ginger powder
- 4 cups vegetable broth
- 1 large shallot, chopped
- 4 tsp camu camu powder
- 2 medium beets, cubes
- ½ cup coconut milk
- Juice of half a lime

Add the shallot, oil to a pot and sauté for 2 min. Add broth, camu camu powder, ginger, beets, salt to taste. Simmer 15 min. Add the coconut milk, simmer 5 min. Stir in lime juice.

4
Servings

8
ingredients

22 min
to cook

Health Benefits of

SHIITAKE MUSHROOM

May support immune system

May improve digestion

May support heart health

Helps boost overall energy

May support bone health
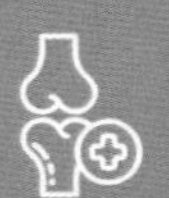

May support brain health
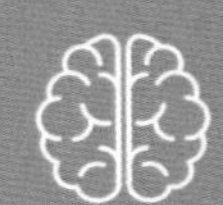

May improve skin health
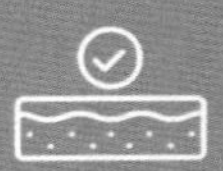

Antibacterial and antiviral effects

HOW TO EAT & DRINK

Sauté
or roast them

Add Shiitake powder
to coffee, tea, smoothie

Cook
soups

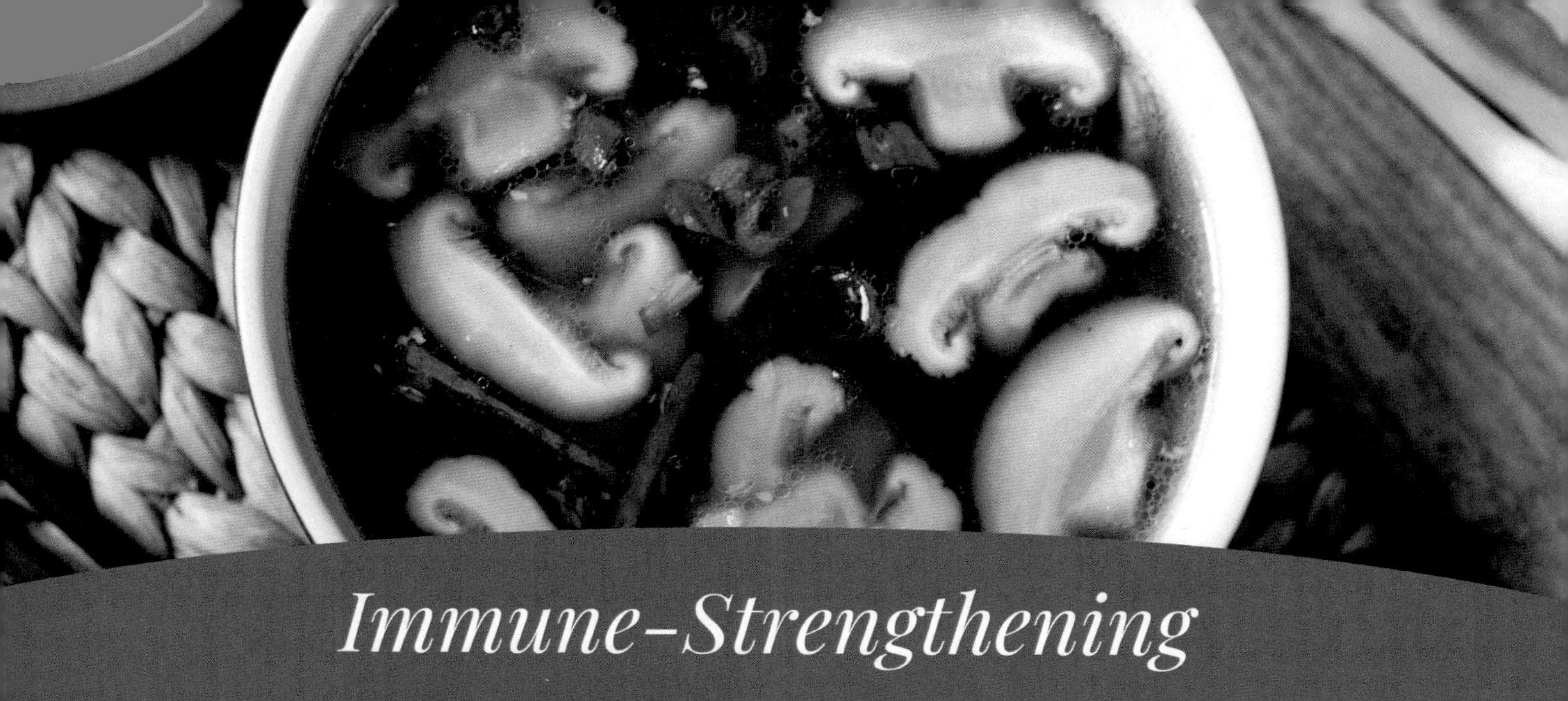

Immune-Strengthening

SHIITAKE SOUP

- 1 tbsp sesame oil
- 1 tsp grated ginger
- 1 tbsp soy sauce
- 6 oz silken tofu, cubes
- ½ cup shallots, chopped
- 3 green onions, chopped
- 2 ½ cups shiitake mushrooms, sliced
- 4 cups vegetable broth

Add the shallots, sesame oil to a pot, cook 3 min. Add mushrooms, cook 5 min. Add broth, soy sauce, ginger. Simmer for 15 minutes. Serve with green onions and tofu.

4
Servings

8
ingredients

23 min
to cook

Health Benefits of

BEETROOT

May improve athletic performance

Supports energy levels

May reduce inflammation

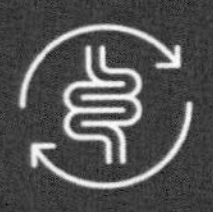
May improve digestive health

May help manage blood pressure

Many nutrients & few calories

May support liver health

Helps maintain a healthy weight

HOW TO EAT & DRINK

Blend
into a smoothie

Add
to salads

Pickle
beets

Cook
soups & sauces

Nutritious and Delicious

BEETROOT SOUP

- 1 tbsp olive oil
- 1 onion, diced
- ½ tsp thyme leaves
- 1 tsp ground cumin
- 2 medium beets, cubes
- 3 sweet potatoes, cubes
- 4 cups vegetable broth
- ½ tsp paprika powder
- 2 cloves garlic, minced
- 2 tbsp balsamic vinegar

Add the diced onion, garlic, oil, cook 3 min. Add beets, potatoes, broth, cumin, paprika, thyme leaves. Simmer for 20 min. Blend with immersion blender. Add vinegar, salt, pepper to taste.

4
Servings

10
ingredients

23 min
to cook

Health Benefits of

LION'S MANE

May reduce stress

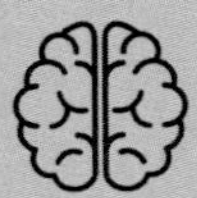
May support brain health

May support gut health

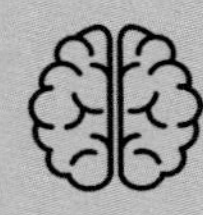
May protect against dementia

May support immune system

May relieve mild anxiety

May reduce inflammation

May aid in blood sugar regulation

HOW TO EAT & DRINK

Sauté
or roast them

Add Lion's Mane powder
to coffee, tea, smoothie

Cook
soups

Brain-Boosting Lion's Mane CHOWDER

- 2 tbsp olive oil
- 1 onion, diced
- 1 tsp fresh thyme
- 1 cup sour cream
- 2 cloves garlic, minced
- 5 russet potatoes, chopped
- 4 cups vegetable broth
- 2 cups Lion's Mane mushrooms, sliced

Add the onion, garlic, oil to a pot, cook 3 min. Add mushrooms, thyme, potatoes, cook 5 min. Add broth. Cook for 10 min. Add the cream. Simmer 5 min. Season with salt, pepper to taste.

4
Servings

8
ingredients

23 min
to cook

Health Benefits of
OREGANO

May support immune system

Could help relieve pain

Helps reduce viral infection

Could help treat yeast infections

May help with sore throat & cough

May reduce inflammation

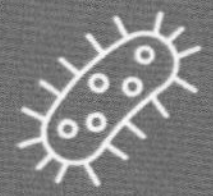
May help fight bacteria

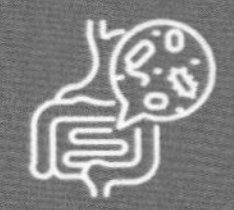
May support gut health

HOW TO EAT & DRINK

Make
oregano tea

Add
to salads

Finish
pasta with leaves

Cook
soups & sauces

Cold and Flu Buster Oregano
MEXICAN SOUP

- 2 tbsp olive oil
- 1 tsp ground cumin
- 2 tsp dried oregano
- 4 cups chicken broth
- 1 red bell pepper, diced
- 1 (4 oz) can green chiles
- ¼ tsp red pepper flakes
- 2 cloves garlic, minced
- 1 (15 oz) can kidney beans
- 1 cup tomatoes
- ½ cup frozen corn

Add bell pepper, garlic, oil to a pot, cook 5 min. Stir in the cumin, oregano, pepper flakes, salt to taste, cook 1 min. Add broth, beans, tomatoes, chiles, and corn. Simmer 15 min.

4
Servings

11
ingredients

21 min
to cook

Health Benefits of BASIL

May improve skin health

May improve digestion

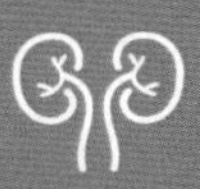
May help with kidney stones

Helps fight a range of infections

May aid in blood sugar regulation

May support liver health

May support eye health

May reduce inflammation

HOW TO EAT & DRINK

Make basil tea

Add to salads

Finish pasta with leaves

Cook soups & sauces

Disease-Fighting Basil

TOMATO SOUP

- 2 tbsp olive oil
- 1 onion, chopped
- ½ cup basil, chopped
- ½ cup sour cream
- 2 cloves garlic, minced
- 2 (14.5 oz) cans diced tomatoes
- 2 cups vegetable broth
- 1 tbsp balsamic vinegar

Add onion, garlic, oil to a pot, cook 3 min. Add tomatoes and broth. Simmer for 15 minutes. Stir in basil, salt to taste, vinegar. Puree the soup with immersion blender. Serve with sour cream.

4
Servings

8
ingredients

18 min
to cook

Health Benefits of

GARLIC

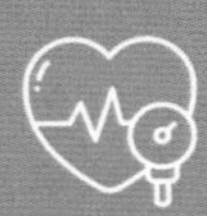
May help manage blood pressure

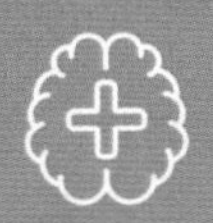
May prevent Alzheimer's

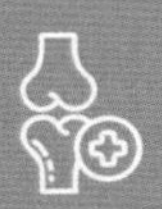
May support bone health

Helps protect against cold & flu

May support immune system

Rich in antioxidants

May support heart health

May support brain health
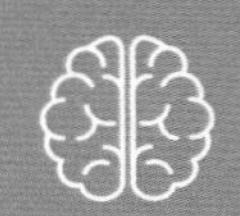

HOW TO EAT GARLIC

Garnish your sandwich

Add to salads

Mix it into pastas

Cook soups & sauces

Gut Healing Garlic

BROCCOLI SOUP

- 2 tbsp butter
- 2 tbsp olive oil
- 3 cloves garlic, minced
- 2 bunches asparagus, cut into pieces
- 4 cups vegetable broth
- 1 head broccoli, cut into florets

Heat the butter, oil in a pot. Add garlic, cook 2 min. Add asparagus, cook 3 min. Add broth, broccoli. Simmer 15 min. Season with salt, pepper to taste. Puree with immersion blender.

4
Servings

6
ingredients

20 min
to cook

Health Benefits of

MACA

May support gut health

May reduce stress

May lift your mood

May help with depression

May improve memory and aid learning

May improve libido

May help with male fertility

May boost energy, sports performance

HOW TO EAT & DRINK

Add in
energy balls

Make
maca latte

Bake
with maca powder

Cook
soups & sauces

Energy-Boosting Sweet Potato

MACA SOUP

- 1 onion, diced
- ¼ cup coconut milk
- 1 tsp ground cumin
- 1 tsp smoked paprika
- 2 sweet potatoes, cubes
- 1 clove garlic, minced
- 2 tbsp maca powder
- 4 cups vegetable broth

Add the onion, garlic, 1 tbsp water, cook 2 min. Add potatoes, cumin, smoked paprika, broth. Simmer 15 min. Stir in the maca powder, coconut milk, salt to taste. Puree with immersion blender.

4
Servings

8
ingredients

17 min
to cook

Health Benefits of

MATCHA

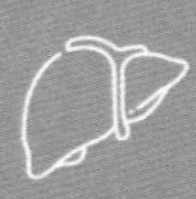
May support liver health

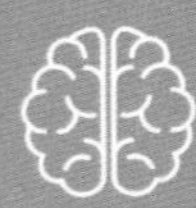
May support brain health

May support heart health

Can make you more productive

May improve skin health

May help fight off infections

Promotes calmness

Helps maintain a healthy weight

HOW TO EAT & DRINK

Blend
into a smoothie

Make
matcha tea

Bake
with matcha

Cook
soups & sauces

Metabolism-Boosting Matcha

THAI SOUP

- Juice of 1 lime
- 1 tbsp matcha
- 1 tbsp fish sauce
- 1 tbsp grated ginger
- 1 stalk lemongrass
- 2 cloves garlic, minced
- 2 white potatoes, cubes
- 1 red chili pepper, chopped
- 2 cups light coconut milk
- 2 cups vegetable broth

Heat the coconut milk, broth in a pot. Add matcha, fish sauce, potatoes, garlic, ginger, lemongrass, lime juice, salt to taste, chili pepper, simmer 15 min.

4
Servings

10
ingredients

18 min
to cook

Health Benefits of
BRAZIL NUTS

May support thyroid function

May support heart health

May improve digestion

May reduce inflammation

Helps maintain a healthy weight

May promote hair growth

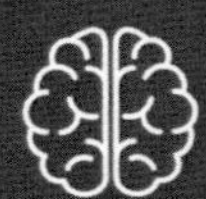
May support brain health

May improve skin health

HOW TO EAT & DRINK

Blend
into a smoothie

Add in
energy balls

Make
nut milk

Cook
soups & sauces

Brain-Boosting Brazil Nut

RAW SOUP

- ⅓ cup brazil nuts
- 2 tbsp olive oil
- 1 onion, chopped
- 1 cup coconut milk
- ½ tsp cumin
- ¼ tsp coriander
- 2 cloves garlic, minced
- 2 cups carrots, chopped
- ¼ tsp turmeric powder
- 4 cups vegetable broth

Transfer all ingredients to a blender and blend until smooth. Divide the soup into serving bowls and season with salt and pepper to taste. Serve cold.

4
Servings

10
ingredients

2 min
to cook

Made in the USA
Las Vegas, NV
21 April 2024